SHIRE NATURAL HI

GW0040028

LAND SN
of the British Isles

A. A. WARDHAUGH

CONTENTS

Cover: *Arianta arbustorum, the Copse Snail.*

Series editor: Jim Flegg.

Copyright © 1989 by A. A. Wardhaugh. First published 1989.
Number 45 in the Shire Natural History series. ISBN 0 7478 0027 8.
All rights reserved. No part of this publication may be reproduced or transmitted in any form or by any means, electronic or mechanical, including photocopy, recording, or any information storage and retrieval system, without permission in writing from the publishers, Shire Publications Ltd, Cromwell House, Church Street, Princes Risborough, Aylesbury, Bucks HP17 9AJ, UK.

Printed in Great Britain by C. I. Thomas & Sons (Haverfordwest) Ltd, Press Buildings, Merlins Bridge, Haverfordwest, Dyfed.

Introduction

Land snails are easily overlooked but with a little searching many of the ninety or so species occurring in the British Isles are not difficult to find. Their diversity of form, notably in the colour, shape and texture of the shell, both between and within species, makes them a fascinating group of animals. Indeed, extensive studies of variation in one of the most common British species, the Brown-lipped Banded Snail (*Cepaea nemoralis*), has contributed significantly to our knowledge of natural selection, the principal driving force of evolution. Compared to the larger groups of arthropods, for example, moths, beetles and spiders, there are far fewer species of land snail in Britain, making their identification less difficult. A knowledge of the land snails occurring in an area can be of value for conservation since some act as indicator species. For example, the presence of certain types of snail in a woodland would suggest that it is of great age and therefore its other fauna and flora are likely to be diverse, unusual and worthy of conservation. Most British land snails are herbivorous, feeding on lichens, fungi or decaying rather than fresh vegetation. Consequently they do not often become pests of food crops and are in general a harmless group of animals.

STRUCTURE

Although land snails vary a good deal in shape and size, all have the same basic design. They possess a spirally coiled shell into which the body can be withdrawn to provide protection from both predators and desiccation. The shell is composed of two fused layers. The inner layer, or ostracum, is made of calcium carbonate (chalk) and is relatively thick in most species. Covering this is the periostracum, which is translucent, horny and usually thinner, being made of a protein called conchiolin. Thickness of the ostracum varies considerably between species; the thinner the ostracum the more translucent the shell appears. Both layers may contain coloured pigments. When a snail hatches from its egg it already has a small shell, the protoconch, and as the animal grows new material is added to this at the lip. Growth tends to be irregular and this results in the presence of unevenly spaced transverse growth ridges on the shells of many species. Damage to the shell can be made good by the deposition of material in the region of fractures and occasionally shells show signs of extensive repair. In the adults of many species the shell becomes thickened in the region of the lip to provide strength. Just inside it there may be nodules or ridges called teeth, which may help to exclude predators such as beetles when the snail withdraws. The periostracum wears away with time, notably from old empty shells and from shells of snails living in sandy areas such as dunes, as a result of abrasion. Such shells appear faded and can be completely white. When a snail has withdrawn into its shell, it may secrete a film of mucus over the mouth. This film, called the epiphragm, is usually thin and transparent but when hibernating some larger species form one which is thicker and opaque. (Many species of snail hibernate, becoming inactive during cold weather in winter.) Compared with the exoskeleton of insects, the shell of a snail may seem a rather cumbersome form of protection but it has the advantage of growing with the animal, making moulting unnecessary. The new exoskeleton of an insect is soft for some time after moulting, rendering the animal very vulnerable to predators during this period.

In most types of snail the shell is dextrally coiled: in other words if it is held upright with the shell mouth facing the observer then the mouth is on the right. If the mouth is on the left the shell is said to be sinistral. Each coil of the shell is called a whorl, the groove between adjacent whorls being known as the suture. In some species the shell is angled around the outer edge of the last whorl and is said to be keeled. On the underside of the shell there is sometimes an opening running up the central axis. This opening is called the umbilicus.

The body of a snail is divided into two main areas, a proportionately large, muscular foot on which the animal crawls and the visceral mass which is within the

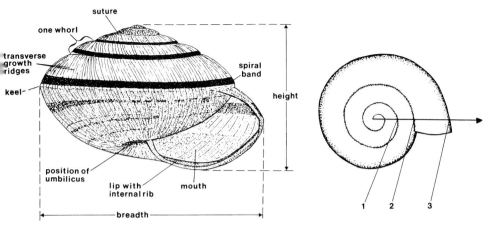

1 (above left). *Parts of a snail shell. Cernuella virgata, the Striped Snail (width 12 mm).*

2 (above right). *Counting the whorls of a snail shell.*

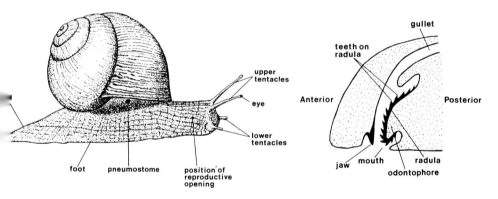

3 (above left). *External features of the Roman Snail, Helix pomatia.*

4 (above right). *Vertical section (diagrammatic) through the head of a snail, showing the jaw and radula.*

shell. The visceral mass contains much of the digestive tract and reproductive organs. Land snails possess a distinct head which bears two pairs of tentacles in most species, with simple eyes at the tips of the upper, larger pair. The tentacles can be withdrawn by inversion, a process much like the finger of a glove being pulled inside out. The roof of the mouth has a jaw in the form of a transverse hardened plate. A tongue-like structure, the odontophore, bears a toothed surface called the radula which functions as a rasp, scraping against the jaw. In an active snail, an opening is often visible on the body wall, near to the shell mouth. This is called the pneumostome and it leads into a space, the mantle cavity, which acts as a lung. The pneumostome opens and the floor of the mantle cavity is lowered in order to draw air in. The pneumostome is then closed and the mantle cavity floor raised to increase air pressure and so assist the uptake of oxygen into the blood. Surprisingly the anus and urinary tract open near to the pneumostome and, in order to conserve water, urine is excreted in a semi-solid

3

form. The reproductive opening is a little way behind the right tentacle in dextrally coiled snails (behind the left in sinistral species).

The lower surface of the foot, on which the snail crawls, is called the sole. If a snail is allowed to crawl on a sheet of glass and is viewed from below, waves of muscular contraction can be seen passing forward over the surface of the sole, in other words in the same direction as the animal moves. These waves take the form of alternating light and dark bands. The light bands are the areas in contact with the glass and are stationary, whilst the narrower dark bands are the zones raised from the surface and undergoing forward movement. At the front end of the sole, just behind the mouth, is the opening of the pedal gland. This organ secretes the thick mucus on which the animal crawls. The mucus allows the stationary light bands of the sole to adhere to the substratum. Indeed its adhesive properties are such that snails are well able to crawl up vertical surfaces.

Snails are not as well adapted to life on land as are many arthropods, notably insects. They are prone to desiccation because the secretion of mucus during locomotion involves the loss of much water. Moreover the skin of snails is moist and not at all waterproof, in marked contrast to the insect cuticle. Not surprisingly snails are most active at night or on warm, still, moist days. In dry weather they become inactive, most seeking out humid places away from predators, such as beneath stones or logs or amid leaf litter, beneath loose bark or in crevices in rock faces or stone walls. They can remain inactive throughout prolonged periods of adverse weather such as long dry spells in summer or periods of low temperature in winter.

CLASSIFICATION AND EVOLUTION

The animal kingdom is divided into a series of major groups called phyla. The two most familiar of these are perhaps the phylum Chordata, which includes all backboned animals (vertebrates), and the phylum Arthropoda (insects, spiders, crustaceans and their allies). Land snails belong to the phylum Mollusca (the molluscs), *mollis* meaning soft-bodied, a very diverse group characterised by the possession of a soft, unsegmented body, usually a muscular foot and often a shell. There are about eighty thousand living species, making it the second largest animal phylum as arthropods probably number well over a million species, possibly far more. In contrast there are no more than about forty thousand species of chordate. Molluscs are divided into six classes, the largest being the gastropods (meaning stomach foot), which includes all snails and slugs, both terrestrial and aquatic. The other molluscan classes include bivalves such as the oyster and mussel, chitons, tusk shells, octopuses, cuttlefish and squid.

Probably the best approach to understanding the body plan of land snails is to consider the likely appearance of the first molluscs, which evolved in the seas of the pre-Cambrian period over six hundred million years ago. It is thought that these animals had a low, rounded or conical shell, making them superficially limpet-like in appearance (present-day limpets, however, are not primitive in body plan and not closely related to ancestral molluscs). They fed by scraping microscopic algae from rock surfaces in shallow water, their digestive tract having the anus opening into a space at the hind end of the body called the mantle cavity. This cavity housed a pair of gills for respiration.

During the evolution of gastropods two significant changes to this body plan took place. One of these was a process called torsion, something which occurs in the embryonic development of present-day gastropods and is not found in any other group of molluscs. This involved most of the internal organs behind the head being twisted anticlockwise through 180 degrees so that the mantle cavity, gills and anus came to lie at the front of the body, just behind the head. The digestive tract was then approximately U-shaped, as is the case in land snails. One advantage to this arrangement was that it allowed much more room inside the shell for the withdrawal of the head and the foot. In addition the head could be withdrawn first, something which was of great value in avoiding predators. Moreover, it

4

5 and 6. *Helix aspersa, the Common Snail, viewed from above (left), viewed from below (right), crawling on a glass plate. Note the muscular waves, visible as transverse bands, passing along the sole of the foot.*

meant that the head, and therefore the brain and sense organs, could then become proportionately larger. It also allowed the gills of these marine gastropods to receive a current of clean water from in front of the animal rather than disturbed silt-laden water from behind.

The other major change was in the shape of the shell, which became progressively more conical in order to accommodate increasing body size, and then spirally coiled to make it less cumbersome. Initially it was coiled in one plane (a planospiral) and only later in evolution did it become conically wound as in most present-day gastropods, an arrangement which makes it much more compact.

The gastropod class is divided into three sub-classes, the Prosobranchia, which includes marine snails such as the winkle and whelk, the Opisthobranchia (sea slugs) and the Pulmonata, to which most land snails and slugs belong. Prosobranchs are typically marine but there are some freshwater and terrestrial forms. In Britain two species of land snail belong to this group, *Pomatias elegans*, the Round-mouthed Snail, and *Acicula fusca*, the Point Shell. They are typical prosobranchs in possessing a single pair of tentacles with eyes at their bases and

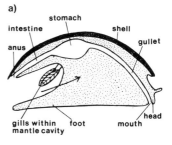

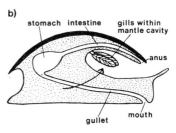

7. *(a) Ancestral gastropod, a marine snail, with the mantle cavity containing the gills at the posterior. (b) After torsion, with the mantle cavity at the anterior. Later in evolution, as snails colonised the land, the gills were lost and the mantle cavity was modified to form an air-breathing lung.*

5

also an operculum, which is a horny or calcareous plate borne on the tail and used to seal off the entrance of the shell when the animal withdraws. All other British land snails are pulmonates, a group which undoubtedly evolved from seashore prosobranchs that colonised the land. They typically lack an operculum and do not have gills. Instead the mantle cavity has evolved to form a lung. Most pulmonates have two pairs of tentacles, with the eyes at the tips of the posterior (upper) pair. One family of pulmonates, the Door Snails (Clausiliidae), possesses a spoon-shaped plate (a clausilium) which closes off the entrance to the shell. This has evolved quite independently of the prosobranch operculum.

The name 'slug' is generally applied to shell-less snails, all terrestrial slugs in Britain being pulmonates. Reduction in shell size and sometimes its eventual loss is a trend which has occurred several times in the evolution of gastropods and there are no less than three quite unrelated groups of slug species in Britain.

REPRODUCTION

Pulmonate snails are hermaphrodite, which means that each adult individual has both male and female reproductive organs. When they mate, each partner transfers sperm to the other and hence all adults are capable of laying eggs. Courtship behaviour has been described in some but by no means all species, the general pattern being as follows. Individuals locate one another possibly by scent or by one snail following the mucus trail of another. The two partners then circle around one another, each touching the other with its tentacles. Individuals of

several species, for example *Cepaea nemoralis*, the Brown-lipped Banded Snail, have a most bizarre courtship ritual. As part of the reproductive system, they possess an internal organ called a dart sac which secretes and contains a calcareous spicule, sometimes referred to as a love dart. Whilst the animals are circling they each extrude a dart through the reproductive opening and drive it quite forcefully into the skin of the partner. The precise reason for this unusual piece of behaviour is not known, but it may act as a stimulus for the exchange of sperms which is the next stage in the process. Later a new dart may form in the dart sac since individuals of some species mate several times.

Next the pair position themselves facing in opposite directions so that their reproductive openings are in close proximity. Each has a penis which is everted through the opening and inserted into that of the partner, where it is placed in the vagina. Spermatozoa are thus exchanged between the two individuals simultaneously. The seminal fluid is enclosed in a long narrow tough envelope made of chitin and it is this sperm packet, or spermatophore, which is transferred during insemination. Once the spermatophore is in the body of the recipient, the chitin envelope is broken down and the liberated sperms are able to fertilise the eggs. These are usually laid about two weeks after mating, though seminal fluid can be stored for as much as a year or more in some species before it is used for fertilisation. The duration of courtship and mating varies with species and individuals from a few minutes to several hours.

Notable exceptions to the above pattern are the two prosobranch land snails,

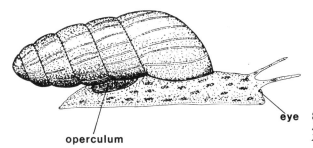

eye

operculum

8. *Acicula fusca*, the Point Shell, a land prosobranch (shell 2.5 mm long).

Pomatias elegans, the Round-mouthed Snail, and *Acicula fusca*, the Point Shell. These two species are not hermaphrodite, the sexes being separate.

The smallest snail species often lay their eggs singly but medium-sized and larger snails lay them in clusters of anything from about ten to two hundred. The eggs are spherical, up to about 3 mm in diameter in larger species and usually transparent with a soft, flexible coat. In some types of snail, however, there is a chalky shell. The coat is not waterproof so the eggs must be laid in moist places to prevent desiccation but they can withstand a good deal of water loss without harm. Most species lay their eggs in spring or summer in suitable moist places at ground level, such as beneath logs or stones, amid leaf litter or in small cavities which the parent makes in the soil. The eggs are not cared for by the parent and consequently many are eaten by predators and others may dry out if conditions become unfavourable. Rate of development is very dependent on temperature but normally the eggs hatch within a few weeks. The young snails resemble the adults but are much smaller and have shells consisting of fewer whorls. Most species grow to maturity in about a year, breed and then die, but larger species can take two to four years to mature and may live for ten years or more.

DIET AND PREDATORS

The majority of snails are herbivorous, feeding principally on decaying vegetation including rotting wood and also on fungi, lichens and algae. In contrast to many insects, such as caterpillars of the Lepidoptera, there are no known specific associations between snail species and particular food plants. Snails can be reared quite easily on artificial diets such as moistened rolled oats or bran, carrot, potato and other root vegetables. A few species are known to have some dietary specialisations, for example, *Punctum pygmaeum*, the Dwarf Snail, feeds chiefly on rotting wood and *Cecilioides acicula*, the subterranean Blind Snail, burrows through the soil consuming hyphae, the fine thread-like structures making up the tissues of fungi. Snails will often climb

considerable distances up tree trunks, rock outcrops and old stone walls in order to graze on surface coverings of lichens and algae.

Many snail species will eat carrion if they encounter it. Some, for example *Discus rotundatus*, the Rounded Snail, and *Euconulus fulvus*, the Tawny Snail, have been observed rasping at the surface of discarded egg shells of birds, presumably to obtain supplies of calcium for the production of their own shells. Only a few snails are actively carnivorous. *Vitrina pellucida*, the Pellucid Snail, is known to eat small annelid worms. *Oxychilus alliarius*, the Garlic Snail, and *Oxychilus cellarius*, the Cellar Snail, will consume other small snail species, locating them by following their slime trail and then rasping away at their tissues using the toothed radula and jaw. In captivity these two species will sometimes turn cannibal.

Snails have a variety of predators. Many birds will eat smaller snail species, swallowing them whole. The song thrush (*Turdus philomelos*) habitually locates and carries larger species to a favourite stone and, holding the snail in its bill, hammers it on the stone anvil to break the shell and so extract the animal. Snails commonly predated in this way include *Cepaea nemoralis* and *Cepaea hortensis*, the Banded Snails, and also *Helix aspersa*, the Common Snail, *Arianta arbustorum*, the Copse Snail, and *Monacha cantiana*, the Kentish Snail.

Mammalian predators include hedgehogs, moles, shrews, rats, mice and rabbits. Empty shells resulting from predation by small mammals are distinctive in being broken open around the periphery of the whorls as a result of the animal gnawing away the shell. In contrast those broken by song thrushes typically have the top or one side missing. Snails are also eaten by beetles, notably the larva of *Lampyris noctiluca*, the glow-worm, which feeds almost entirely on snails, including young *Helix aspersa*, the Common Snail. How the insect finds its prey seems to be unknown but it may do so by scent or by following the slime trail. The larva bites and pierces the skin of the snail, pouring a digestive juice into the body of its helpless victim. The snail withdraws into its shell only to be liquefied by the action of the juice. The latter is then drunk by the larva.

Several snail species are polymorphic, that is they exist in more than one form at the same time and in the same locality. Most notable are *Cepaea nemoralis* and *Cepaea hortensis*, the Banded Snails, which have been extensively studied in this respect. Variation is largely inherited, particularly the shell colour and banding patterns. *Cepaea nemoralis* is often eaten by the song thrush, notably in winter when the ground is frozen, making other invertebrates such as earthworms difficult to obtain. It is also taken from May to July when the ground may be dry and hard and the birds have the added problem of young to feed. It is possible to collect the discarded shell fragments from around song thrush anvils and compare the frequency of different varieties with their frequency in the surrounding snail populations. In the past such studies have yielded much interesting information. For example in woodlands, the brown and unbanded pink varieties are common in the snail population but among anvil fragments they form a smaller proportion of the total than would be expected, with high percentages of yellow banded shells present. This is because the brown and pink shells are better camouflaged on a brownish woodland floor, where the yellow banded forms are conspicuous and more often located by song thrushes. In meadows and other grassland areas the reverse is true. Yellow banded forms are well camouflaged among grass stems and at an advantage over other varieties. Interestingly, one study of a hedgerow showed a distinct seasonal change. As the background altered from the browns of winter to spring greens, the yellow banded forms became progressively better camouflaged and fewer were eaten by song thrushes. These studies demonstrate very well the process of natural selection, where some forms of a species survive better than others because they are better suited to their environment. Natural selection is generally considered to be the principal means by which evolutionary change takes place.

Just why so many varieties of this species exist is not easy to explain. It is possible that different forms are at an advantage in different habitats and perhaps at different times of year, hence they all remain in the population and none die out. Polymorphism seems to allow the species to exploit a variety of different habitats. The situation is, however, quite complex for in some downland areas of southern England no such selective effects seem to occur. In France, it has been found that yellow unbanded forms which prevail in open situations are resistant to strong sunlight, whilst pink banded forms are more susceptible and occur more often in shady areas.

The British species

In the following account as many species as possible have been described, including all the most common ones, in an attempt to illustrate the diversity of these animals. Species have been grouped according to the habitat in which they are most likely to be found in the hope that this arrangement will assist the beginner with identification. Some species are not easy to classify in this way and where more than one habitat type is occupied this is indicated. Both scientific and English names are provided although the latter are not in widespread use. All figures following names are typical sizes of adults (height by breadth). Descriptions also refer to adults and it should be remembered that juveniles of species possessing a shell with a thickened lip or rib do not have these features.

WIDESPREAD SNAILS

About a third of British species show no particular association with a major habitat type such as woodland, dry grassland or marsh and in this sense can be described as widespread. In addition the majority of these species are distributed throughout most of Britain.

Helix aspersa, the Common Snail (30 by 30 mm), is one of the best known British species because of its large size and frequent occurrence in gardens. It may be native to south-west Britain but could have been introduced from southern Europe by the Romans as a source of food. The association with gardens and other cultivated areas becomes progressively more marked further northwards in Britain, possibly because these places readily provide suitable hibernation sites such as beneath rockery stones or in wall crevices. If hibernation sites are inspected during early spring, empty shells of both adults and juveniles are not uncommon, indicating that this species finds it difficult to survive the winter in Britain, where it is at the northern limit of its distribution. By day individuals often congregate in suitable hiding places. At night they emerge to feed and habitually return to the same daytime resting place. The globular shell is usually brown or yellowish, often with paler flecks and up to five darker spiral bands. The surface is lightly wrinkled and the mouth bears a white lip. Northwards in Britain the Common Snail becomes strongly associated with coastal dunes, where shells may be virtually white owing to abrasion of the surface by sand particles.

Helix pomatia, the Roman, Apple or Edible Snail (40 by 40 mm), is a closely related species restricted to England south of Northamptonshire. Again it probably owes its presence in Britain to introduction by man. It is less closely associated with gardens than is the Common Snail, being found in woods, coppices, hedgerows and downland but only in calcareous districts. During winter it hibernates for about six months. This is Britain's largest snail, the shell being a pale yellow-brown with coarse transverse ridges and sometimes faint brown spiral bands. It has a very small umbilicus, in contrast to the Common Snail, which lacks one altogether. *Arianta arbustorum*, the Copse Snail (16 by 21 mm), is a related species resembling the Common Snail. The shell is normally brown with paler flecks and a single dark brown spiral band but there is a good deal of variation: some individuals can be quite pale both in shell and body colour. Juveniles are relatively thin-shelled, somewhat keeled and can sometimes be found ascending vegetation. The Copse

9 (above). *Cepaea nemoralis, the Brown-lipped Banded Snail (banded pink variety).*

10 (above). *Cepaea nemoralis, the Brown-lipped Banded Snail, showing variation in the banding patterns of yellow shells.*

11 (below). *Empty shells of Cepaea nemoralis, the Brown-lipped Banded Snail, discarded by predators, the top pair by a brown rat, the bottom pair by a song thrush.*

Snail occurs in most parts of Britain in any fairly moist habitat, often woodland.

Cepaea nemoralis, the Brown-lipped Banded Snail (18 by 22 mm), is a widespread and well known species. Highly variable in appearance, the ground colour of the shell may be straw to almost daffodil yellow, pale to dark pink or brown. It may be bandless or possess up to five brown spiral bands of variable width, two or more of which may be so wide that they are fused. Sometimes the bands are paler and faint or interrupted. The lip is usually dark brown but on occasions it can be paler, even white, causing confusion with its near relative *Cepaea hortensis*, the White-lipped Banded Snail, which is generally smaller (14 by 17 mm) but almost as varied in appearance. In this species the ground colour of the shell is normally yellow, other colours being unusual but, to complicate matters further, the lip can occasionally be brown. Consequently identification of a population of *Cepaea* species should be based on observation of several adult specimens. The two species sometimes occur together, both occupying a wide range of habitats including woods, scrub, grassland and sand dunes, but *Cepaea hortensis* tends to occur in more moist habitats, for example, well vegetated river banks.

Helicigona lapicida, the Lapidiary Snail (8 by 16 mm), is a less common but unmistakable species, having a very flat shell with a most pronounced keel and a broad umbilicus. It is normally light brown with darker transverse markings. Although fairly widespread in calcareous parts of England as far north as Yorkshire, it is absent elsewhere in the British Isles and is declining in range. It becomes active at night and in wet weather, frequenting walls and rocky ground, often in woods. In dry weather it retreats deeply into crevices and becomes very difficult to find. A much more widespread but equally distinctive snail is *Trichia hispida*, the Hairy Snail (5 by 8 mm), so named because the shell has a covering of short hair-like projections. On close inspection these are seen to be curved, which distinguishes it from *Ashfordia granulata*, a much less common woodland species that has straight hairs. Adult Hairy Snails living in drier habitats often lose most of the hairs but some generally remain in and around the moderately large umbilicus. The shell is usually brownish with a white rib just inside the mouth. It does not occur in very dry habitats but is common elsewhere and is often found in gardens. *Trichia striolata*, the Strawberry Snail (9 by 12 mm), is a larger relative which lacks hairs when adult. As its name suggests, it can become a pest on strawberries. The shell varies in colour from red-brown to almost white, often with a pale band around the periphery, and it has fairly coarse, irregularly spaced transverse ridges. This is another species which is probably native only in south-west England, its spread northward being aided by man. It frequently occurs in gardens but is also found in a wide variety of moist shady places.

One of the most common British snails is *Discus rotundatus*, the Rounded Snail (3 by 6 mm), which occurs everywhere except in the driest of habitats. The shell is pale yellow-brown with broad reddish transverse stripes, markings which make it an easy species to recognise. Another distinctive feature is the extremely large umbilicus, which is about one-third of the overall shell diameter. Other common species which have a shell that is much broader than tall include *Oxychilus alliarius*, the Garlic Snail (3 by 6 mm), so named because when touched it emits a strong smell of garlic, possibly as a defence against predators. The shell is a very glossy brown, the animal itself being blue-black. It occurs in a wide range of habitats throughout the British Isles, being quite tolerant of acidic conditions, and hence it is sometimes found in coniferous woodland.

Oxychilus cellarius, the Cellar Snail (5 by 10 mm), also occurs throughout the British Isles but it is a little less tolerant of acidity. The shell is a very pale brown, highly smooth and glossy. The body is pale blue-grey, the mantle being spotted with brown. *Aegopinella nitidula*, the Smooth Snail (4 by 8 mm), is similar to the *Oxychilus* species but the pale brown shell is only slightly translucent and is waxy in appearance rather than glossy. The last whorl increases in diameter quite

12. *Widespread snails. From left to right: (top row) Helicigona lapicida, the Lapidiary Snail x 2; Trichia hispida, the Hairy Snail x 2; Trichia striolata, the Strawberry Snail x 2; (second row) Oxychilus cellarius, the Cellar Snail x 4; Oxychilus alliarius, the Garlic Snail x 4; Aegopinella nitidula, the Smooth Snail x 4; (third row) Vitrina pellucida, the Pellucid Snail x 4; Discus rotundatus, the Rounded Snail x 4; (bottom row) Cochlicopa lubrica, the Slippery Snail x 8; Vitrea crystallina, the Crystal Snail x 8; Euconulus fulvus, the Tawny Snail x 8; Lauria cylindracea, the Chrysalis Snail x 8. (See also figures 3, 5, 9, 13 and cover.)*

noticeably towards the shell mouth and the area around the large umbilicus is often white. This species occurs throughout the British Isles in a wide variety of moderately damp habitats.

Among the smaller discoidal species *Vitrea crystallina*, the Crystal Snail (1.7 by 3.5 mm), is widespread and common. The shell is glossy and colourless but often tinged with green and there is a supporting rib a little way within the mouth. It is composed of about five whorls. *Vitrina pellucida*, the Pellucid Snail (3 by 5 mm), has a very thin greenish transparent shell composed of

about three rapidly expanding whorls. It is most unusual in having a lobe of the mantle reflected up on to the outer surface of the shell. This species matures and breeds in winter and then dies, so generally only old empty shells are to be found during late spring and early summer. It is common and occurs in a wide variety of habitats, sometimes in vast numbers in grassy areas behind sand dunes. Somewhat more top-shaped is *Euconulus fulvus*, the Tawny Snail (2.5 by 3 mm), which has a translucent yellow-brown shell with a low conical spire. Fresh shells are distinctive in having a

11

13 (left). *Cepaea hortensis, the White-lipped Banded Snail, the five-banded yellow variety, one of the commonest forms.*

14 (right). *Four shells which illustrate variation in Cepaea hortensis, the White-lipped Banded Snail.*

silky appearance, the animal itself being a pale grey-brown. It is widespread throughout the British Isles.

The two remaining species are both distinctly taller than broad. *Cochlicopa lubrica*, the Slippery Snail (6 x 2.5 mm), is common and widespread, often occurring amid moss. The translucent brown shell is very glossy and has a red-brown rib at the mouth. *Lauria cylindracea*, the Chrysalis Snail (4 by 2 mm), has a distinctive flat white lip to the otherwise brown shell. It occurs throughout the British Isles in moderately moist sites including gardens, woods, rock outcrops and stone walls. (This species has two similar relatives, *Pupilla muscorum*, characteristic of dry open sites, and *Leiostyla anglica*, found in damp places, chiefly in ancient woodland. See below.)

WOODLAND SNAILS

At the end of the last glacial period a succession of vegetational changes took place in Britain as the climate warmed. This culminated in deciduous woodland, together with its associated fauna, spreading northwards to cover most of the British Isles before the English Channel formed. Thus it is perhaps not surprising that today ancient semi-natural woodland (that is land which has probably never been clear-felled) holds a much greater diversity of mollusc species than other terrestrial habitats. These woodland species require a habitat which provides moisture, shelter, lack of disturbance and, in the majority of cases, the presence of at least some calcium in the soil. Some species have only minimal requirements in these respects and are widespread, being able to live not only in woodland but in other habitats too, such as scrub, hedgerows or even grassland and gardens. In contrast, a few species are restricted entirely to woodland, being much more demanding in their habitat requirements, especially, it seems, with respect to disturbance. Perhaps this is because of their poor powers of dispersal, their populations being very slow to occupy new areas of suitable habitat. These are sometimes referred to as indicator species because their presence

12

15 (left). *Trichia striolata, the Strawberry Snail, showing the pale peripheral band.*

16 (right). *Oxychilus cellarius, the Cellar Snail. Note the very glossy shell of this common species.*

strongly suggests that a woodland is ancient and semi-natural. Between these two distributional extremes exists a spectrum of species restricted to a greater or lesser extent to woodland habitats.

Woodlands vary a great deal. Richest of all in mollusc species are deciduous woods, notably beech, in calcareous areas, where the ground layer is undisturbed and remains moist throughout the year. The presence of marshy areas within the wood, perhaps beside a stream, and also of rocky outcrops, increases the number of species still further to perhaps as many as fifty. In contrast, deciduous woodland on steeply sloping and hence dry ground will have fewer species, especially if the soil is acidic. Conifer plantations, where the thick cover of fallen needles and dense shade prevents the growth of ground vegetation, will yield hardly any molluscs. The practice of coppicing, which began to be revived in Britain during the 1980s, with its attendant disturbance and drying out of the ground layer, does not favour at least some mollusc species.

With respect to identification, it should be remembered that those species described in the section on widespread snails virtually all occur in woodland.

Open woodland or scrub is often home to *Pomatias elegans*, the Round-mouthed Snail (15 by 10 mm), one of the two land prosobranch species occurring in Britain. It has a very thick strong shell, usually greyish or brownish with fine spiral and transverse ribs. The sole of the foot is divided longitudinally into two halves which can be moved independently when crawling. This species has the habit of burrowing and is found only in areas of loose, very calcareous soils in the southern half of Britain. It is declining in numbers possibly as a result of long-term climatic cooling or changes in soil conditions, but where present it can be locally abundant. Britain's other land prosobranch, *Acicula fusca*, the Point Shell (2.5 by 0.8 mm), is found in damper parts of old woods but is very locally distributed. The glossy shell is a beautiful translucent golden brown. Unique among British snails, it has a

13

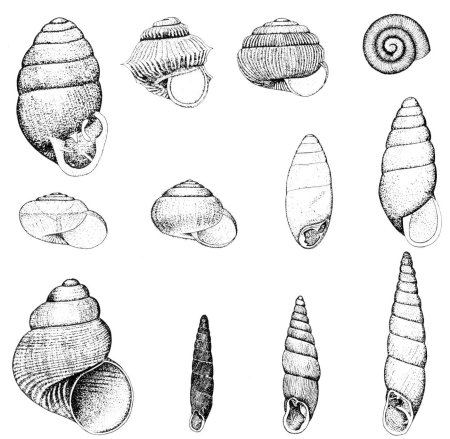

17. *Woodland snails. From left to right: (top row) Leiostyla anglica, the English Chrysalis Snail x 12; Acanthinula aculeata, the Prickly Snail x 12; Spermodea lamellata, the Plaited Snail x 12; Punctum pygmaeum, the Dwarf Snail x 12; (second row) Zenobiella subrufescens, the Brown Snail x 3; Ashfordia granulata, the Silky Snail x 3; Azeca goodalli, the Three-toothed Snail x 5; Ena obscura, the Lesser Bulin x 5; (bottom row) Pomatias elegans, the Round-mouthed Snail x 3; Clausilia bidentata, the Door Snail x 3; Macrogastra rolphii, , Rolph's Door Snail x 3; Cochlodina laminata, the Plaited Door Snail x 3. (See also figure 8.)*

series of transverse grooves which are widely and unevenly spaced. Unlike all other British land snails, these two species are not hermaphrodite, the sexes being separate.

Acanthinula aculeata, the Prickly Snail (2 by 2 mm), is a small species of unusual appearance. It has a dark brown shell with regularly spaced transverse ridges drawn out to form large spines around the periphery. These tend to collect debris, making the animal well camouflaged amid leaf litter. Although widespread in woodlands, scrub and hedge-

rows, this snail never seems to occur in high densities. In older specimens the spines become worn down and it could then be confused with *Spermodea lamellata*, the Plaited Snail (2 by 2 mm), a near relative which is much more uncommon and locally distributed. It is almost entirely confined to northern parts of Britain and Ireland, being restricted to leaf litter in old deciduous woods. Fresh specimens have a most striking iridescent appearance due to the shell having a series of fine transverse ribs which are closely and very regularly spaced. The shell is a much

14

paler, more golden brown than that of *Acanthinula aculeata*, and the mouth is not thickened.

Leiostyla anglica, the English Chrysalis Snail (3.5 by 2 mm), is another indicator of ancient semi-natural woodland. It is sparsely distributed in northern and western Britain, occurring in damp places in woods and sometimes around marshes. The shell is a distinctive rich red-brown colour, the mouth edge being strongly thickened with up to six teeth. *Azeca goodalli*, the Three-toothed Snail (6 by 2.5 mm), occurs in moss and leaf litter locally in England and Wales. It may be found in scrub and hedgerows as well as in woodland. The brown shell is extremely glossy, the flat-sided whorls providing a distinctive outline. Of somewhat similar proportions is *Ena obscura*, the Lesser Bulin (8 by 4 mm), which has a conical brown shell bearing a white lip with no teeth. It is fairly common, occurring in woodland, scrub and also rocky places.

One of the smallest woodland species is *Punctum pygmaeum*, the Dwarf Snail (0.8 by 1.5 mm). Preferring more moist areas of leaf litter, this minute disc-shaped snail feeds on decaying wood. The shell is composed of 3½ whorls and is golden brown, possessing a sheen in fresh specimens which results from fine regular transverse growth ridges. It is a relative of the widespread snail *Discus rotundatus*, which it resembles quite closely. *Punctum pygmaeum* probably occurs throughout the British Isles but is easily overlooked because of its small size. More locally distributed is *Ashfordia granulata*, the Silky Snail (6 by 8 mm), which has a shell bearing short hair-like spines. Careful examination with a hand lens reveals that these are straight and arise from bulbous bases. The globular shell is thin, translucent and pale brown to grey-yellow, having a minute umbilicus. This snail could be confused with the much more common *Trichia hispida* (see 'Widespread snails'). Of similar shape but lacking hairs is *Zenobiella subrufescens*, the Brown Snail (6 by 9 mm), in which the slightly glossy, pale brown shell is so thin that it is quite flexible. Intolerant of human disturbance, this species is characteristic of damper parts of old woodland in northern and western Bri-

tain. In warmer weather it climbs vegetation, sometimes being associated with the Great Wood-rush (*Luzula sylvatica*) and Butterbur (*Petasites hybridus*).

The Door Snails (Clausiliidae) have shells which are sinistrally coiled and, being brown and spindle-shaped, they bear more than a passing resemblance to beech buds. By day these species usually remain hidden in leaf litter but at night or in warm damp weather they emerge, often climbing high up exposed surfaces such as tree trunks to feed on lichens and algae. The most common is *Clausilia bidentata*, the Door Snail (10 by 2.5 mm), which is widespread, occurring in hedgerows, among rocks and on old walls as well as in woodland. *Cochlodina laminata*, the Plaited Door Snail (16 by 4 mm), is almost entirely restricted to England. *Macrogastra rolphii*, Rolph's Door Snail (13 by 3.5 mm), is found only in southern England. Proportionately shorter and broader than the other species, it does not climb to feed.

SNAILS OF DRIER HABITATS

This group of habitats includes coastal sand dunes, chalk downland, rocky outcrops, screes, walls and similar sites. Such areas are not only drier but at times much warmer than adjacent woodland and for these reasons they are more difficult places for molluscs to inhabit. Many of the widespread species are absent, their place being taken by specialists adapted to live in these harsh conditions. For example many species become inactive (aestivate) during the driest weather of summer and only emerge when the air is sufficiently humid. Several breed in the autumn and early winter so that the eggs and young avoid the heat of summer. Their young are resistant to low temperatures and so can remain active and grow during much of the winter. Dry open habitats have fewer species than old woodland but those present are often abundant. A few of the species described in 'Widespread snails' may occur in dry habitats, notably the Banded Snails (*Cepaea nemoralis* and *Cepaea hortensis*) and the Common Snail (*Helix aspersa*).

One of the larger and more noticeable species in open habitats is *Monacha cantiana*, the Kentish Snail (12 by 16 mm). It is not well named since it is quite widespread in England, although more common in the south and east. Its range seems to be expanding, however. The shell varies in colour from an off-white to a brownish or reddish pink, often darker nearer the mouth, with a paler spiral band around the periphery. In adults the shell mouth has a white internal rib and there is a small umbilicus. This species inhabits long grass (for example roadside verges), scrub and occasionally sand dunes.

Cernuella virgata, the Striped Snail (6 to 19 by 8 to 25 mm but typically 8 by 15 mm), is highly variable in both size and appearance, but its fairly globular shape distinguishes it from similar thick-shelled species. The shell is most often white with a single dark brown spiral band and sometimes fainter bands on the underside. This and the next three species described are typically found in dunes or short calcareous grassland and are generally more common in southern Britain and nearer the sea. *Candidula intersecta*, the Wrinkled Snail (6.5 by 10 mm), has a more flattened shell than the Striped Snail, with strong transverse growth ridges. It is white to ginger with dark brown spiral bands, often blotchy or interrupted and more distinct on the lower surface. The mouth has a strong white internal rib. *Candidula gigaxii*, the Eccentric Snail (6 by 10 mm), is very similar but the shell has only fine transverse ridges and the last half whorl is comparatively broad. Its English name refers to the umbilicus in which the axis is not central. Compared to the Wrinkled Snail, it occurs more often in taller herbage, often climbing plant stems (for example umbellifers), and is said to feed sometimes on decaying thistle flowers. In some districts it relies heavily on hedgerows as a habitat and with their removal it has declined in numbers. *Helicella itala*, the Heath Snail (9 by 18 mm), tends to occupy warm steep slopes, being most active in summer and early autumn. It is very variable in size and appearance but most commonly white with a single dark brown spiral band. The umbilicus is unusually large, being about one-third of the overall shell diameter.

Similar to this group of species is *Theba*

pisana, the Sandhill Snail (15 by 18 mm), again variable in size and appearance but most attractive. It is common around the Mediterranean but rare in Britain, occurring only on the coast in parts of South Wales, Cornwall, the Channel Islands and eastern Ireland. It seems to make little effort to avoid heat on sunny days, often remaining on vegetation in an exposed position.

Of the smaller species *Pyramidula rupestris*, the Rock Snail (1.5 by 2.5 mm), tends to be locally distributed but often abundant where it occurs. It inhabits rock outcrops and drystone walls chiefly in calcareous districts. In dry weather it retires to crevices and the undersides of stones. The shell has pronounced transverse striations and is brown or purplish, often bleached grey or off-white in older specimens. The umbilicus is very broad, being more than a third of the shell diameter. *Vallonia costata*, the Ribbed Snail (1.2 by 2.5 mm), occupies similar habitats but also dry grassland and dunes. It is less common in northern Britain. The grey-white shell has large, regularly spaced transverse white ribs which in fresh specimens make it iridescent in bright sunlight. The shell mouth has a very thick white lip. This species has two close relatives, *Vallonia excentrica* and *Vallonia pulchella*. Both lack transverse ribs, the latter generally occupying moist habitats.

Dry-habitat species which are taller than broad include *Balea perversa*, the Tree Snail (8 by 2.5 mm). It does occur on trees but only when there is moss or loose bark under which it can hide. It is not found in extensive woodland, rather on woodland edges or in hedgerow trees. More often it occurs on rock outcrops and drystone walls. Specimens from Scotland are on average larger than those from the south. The Tree Snail is a member of the clausiliid family (see 'Woodland snails') and, being sinistrally coiled and widest at the body whorl, it is similar to juveniles of other species in this group but can be distinguished by colour. The shells of other species are dark or reddish brown whereas the Tree Snail is a pale yellow-brown. Moreover the shell has a distinctly squarish mouth which generally lacks teeth and there is no

18. *Snails of open habitats. From left to right: (top row) Theba pisana, the Sandhill Snail x 2; Monacha cantiana, the Kentish Snail x 2; Helicella itala, the Heath Snail x 2; (second row) Candidula intersecta, the Wrinkled Snail x 3; (third row) Candidula gigaxii, the Eccentric Snail x 3; Cochicella acuta, the Pointed Snail x 3; Cecilioides acicula, the Blind Snail x 7; Balea perversa, the Tree Snail x 7; (bottom row) Pupilla muscorum, the Moss Snail x 12; Vallonia costata, the Ribbed Snail x 12; Pyramidula rupestris, the Rock Snail x 12; Vertigo pygmaea, a Whorl Snail x 12. (See also figure 1.)*

clausilium. Possibly it does not need these defences against surface dwelling predators such as beetles, because of its habit of living well above ground level. A somewhat smaller species is *Pupilla muscorum*, the Moss Snail (3.5 by 1.7 mm), a relative of *Lauria cylindracea* (see 'Widespread snails'). Less common in the north of Britain, it occurs on short dry calcareous grassland, in stony areas and among sand dunes. The brown shell is unusual in possessing a pale rib on the outside just behind the mouth.

A careful search of the undersides of stones in dry places, old mossy stone walls and similar sites might reveal one of the *Vertigo* species or Whorl Snails. The most widespread of these tiny species in dry habitats is *Vertigo pygmaea* (2 by 1 mm), which has a medium brown shell with a white lip bearing four or five teeth, visible with the aid of a hand lens. Like *Pupilla muscorum* it also has an external transverse rib behind the mouth.

Cecilioides acicula, the Blind Snail (5 by 1.2 mm), lacks eyes, being a subterranean snail living deep in the soil. The empty white shells of this species can sometimes be found on the surface of disturbed soil, for example on mole hills and ant hills.

Cochlicella acuta, the Pointed Snail (10 to 25 by 4 to 7 mm), occurs very largely on dunes on the south and west coasts of Britain and also inland at drier sites in Ireland. Its narrow conical shell is unmistakable in outline but the colour is variable, being white or ginger, often with a brown spiral band on the body whorl below the periphery.

WETLAND SNAILS

Wetlands such as marshes, fens and similar waterlogged areas by lakes, ponds and streams have quite characteristic snail species, many of which do not occur in other habitats. Soil acidity influences the abundance and diversity of species present, base-rich areas providing the best habitats whilst few or no snails will be found in or around acidic peat bogs on moorland. In the wettest sites, some freshwater species may be encountered, notably the Dwarf Pond Snail (*Limnaea*

truncatula). In addition, the empty shells of freshwater species may be found amid old flood debris harbouring land snails. Species inhabiting these intermediate zones where land and fresh water meet are of two quite distinct origins. In Britain the large majority have evolved from fully terrestrial species which have become adapted to wetland life. Two species, however, have an aquatic ancestry. They are the Herald Snails, *Carychium minimum* and *Carychium tridentatum* (approximately 2 by 1 mm), which are similar to freshwater pulmonates in having eyes at the base of the tentacles. *Carychium minimum* is typically a wetland species but *Carychium tridentatum* is more catholic, generally occurring in moist areas. These two species are very similar in appearance, having white shells with a thickened lip bearing three teeth. Other very small snails occurring in wetlands are some of the *Vertigo* species or Whorl Snails (see also 'Snails of drier habitats'). One of the more widespread is *Vertigo substriata* (approximately 2 by 1 mm), distinctive in that the brown shell has fine but regular transverse ridges.

Much more noticeable wetland species are the Amber Snails (family Succineidae). These are considerably larger and often ascend vegetation such as grasses, sedges and yellow flag. *Oxyloma*

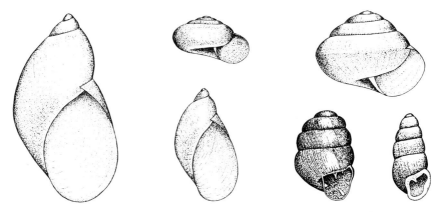

19. *Wetland snails. From left to right: (above) Zonitoides nitidus, the Shiny Snail x 3; Euconulus alderi x 12; (below) Succinea putris, an Amber Snail x 8; Oxyloma pfeifferi, Pfeiffer's Amber Snail x 3; Vertigo substriata, a Whorl Snail x 12; Carychium tridentatum, a Herald Snail x 12.*

pfeifferi, Pfeiffer's Amber Snail (10 by 6 mm), is the most widespread, being common in suitable habitats throughout all of the British Isles except parts of north-west Scotland. The translucent glossy shell is amber to light brown in colour and in adults it is composed of about three whorls which expand very rapidly. The animal is usually a dark grey colour but it can be paler, making it hard to distinguish from the other widespread species, *Succinea putris*, the Amber Snail (16 by 10 mm), which is normally dull yellow but sometimes darker. The shell of the latter is generally greenish yellow and it occurs in slightly drier places, for example moist grassland, although the two species are sometimes found together. Three other much less common members of this family occur in Britain and the five species can only be distinguished with certainty on the basis of differences in anatomy.

There are two other widespread snail species which are characteristic of wetland. One is *Euconulus alderi* (2 by 2.5 mm), which differs from its close relative *Euconulus fulvus* (see 'Widespread snails') in being slightly smaller and the animal having a dark body. When withdrawn, this makes the glossy brown shell appear virtually black. Larger and more discoidal in shape, *Zonitoides nitidus*, the Shiny Snail (3.5 by 7 mm), is similarly dark-bodied with a glossy brown shell. The mantle bears a distinctive orange spot which can be seen through the shell.

Study and conservation

The foregoing chapter on British snail species provides an indication of general habitats and sites where snails are likely to occur. For a beginner, a garden, park or other open ground to which there is public access could be a suitable place to commence studying snails. Provided it contains some relatively undisturbed areas there should be at least a few species present. Building up a knowledge

of the snails occurring in a limited area is not only interesting in its own right but provides an invaluable core of knowledge which can be used and progressively added to when visiting other areas further afield and richer in molluscs. The species described in the previous sections should be sufficient to assist the beginner with identification. It should be remembered that it is often difficult to name old worn shells or juvenile snails and these are best avoided initially. Inevitably it is not possible to identify every snail one finds.

Equipment required to begin the study of snails is minimal. Useful items include a rule graduated in millimetres, a magnifying glass (or, much better, a hand lens of x 10 or more magnification), an old blunt pocket knife or similar instrument for sifting through fine leaf litter, a small moistened artist's paintbrush for handling the smallest shells and robust plastic containers of various sizes. Lastly, a pocket notebook in which to record findings is indispensable. When searching for snails, take care to cause the minimum degree of disturbance possible. Turn over only a small proportion of stones and logs encountered and replace them carefully after inspection because they are home to innumerable organisms. Always avoid unnecessary trampling of herbage.

Much can be learnt from others who are more knowledgeable, and help can often be gained by contacting local natural history societies or by writing to the Conchological Society of Great Britain and Ireland. This society promotes the study and conservation of molluscs — terrestrial, freshwater and marine. It operates a national recording scheme which has resulted in the production of distribution maps for land snails, an ongoing study that provides much scope for useful contributions by interested field naturalists. Indeed this is perhaps part of the appeal of land snails. So little is known about many aspects of their biology that there is ample opportunity to be a pioneer; the amateur can make significant contributions to knowledge. For example, little detailed information seems to be available on the diet of snails. Most species probably rely on a variety of plants for food but little

20 (above left). *Pomatias elegans, the Round-mouthed Snail. Animal withdrawn and shell mouth closed by the operculum. Compare with figure 8.*

21 (above right). *Cochlodina laminata, the Plaited Door Snail, a distinctive species occurring chiefly in woodland.*

22 (below left). *Monacha cantiana, the Kentish Snail, a fairly common species in open habitats throughout much of England.*

23 (below right). *Candidula intersecta, the Wrinkled Snail, a common species occurring in short calcareous grassland and dunes.*

seems to be known about the spectrum of foods taken by particular snail species or to what extent this varies with season. The activity of snails changes with the weather but again the precise conditions in which different species are active or not seem to be little known. Temperature, humidity, wind strength and light intensity could all be of significance. Lifespan in the wild has not been greatly studied, nor have differences in population density. Where they occur, some species are often abundant whilst others, although occurring throughout most of Britain, are very rarely found at high densities. For example, an hour's careful searching in a suitable habitat for *Acanthinula aculeata*, the Prickly Snail, might well yield only two or three specimens.

In general, a better knowledge of the lifestyles and habitat requirements of snails would be helpful for their conservation. No less than 27 of the ninety or so British snail species are considered to be declining in numbers. In some cases the cause may be the natural warming of the climate since the last glacial period, the species concerned being adapted to cooler or wetter conditions. For other species the problem is often one of habitat loss and disturbance. In particular, the loss of ancient semi-natural woodland and old large hedgerows, and the drainage of wetlands have taken their toll. These habitats are often rich not only in mollusc species but in a wide variety of other wildlife and are generally of great conservation value. Such communities have taken hundreds, possibly thousands, of years to develop and cannot easily be recreated, for example, by tree-planting programmes. So poor are the colonisation powers of some woodland snails that they are often absent from apparently suitable eighteenth-century tree plantations. One could offer reasons why it is of value to save a place in the world for small organisms such as snails, which are of little or no economic benefit: for example, their importance in natural food chains, and their scientific and educational value. Ultimately their conservation is very largely a question of whether we regard them as having some right to existence and whether we feel that their extinction would represent an impoverishment of the world in which we live.

Further reading

Cameron, R. A. D., and Redfern, M. *British Land Snails*. Synopses of the British Fauna (New Series) 6, Linnean Society of London. Academic Press, 1976. (The scientific nomenclature used is at variance with more recent publications but otherwise the book is very useful.)

Kerney, M. P. *Atlas of the Non-marine Mollusca of the British Isles*. Institute of Terrestrial Ecology, Cambridge, 1976.

Kerney, M. P.; Cameron, R. A. D.; and Riley, G. *A Field Guide to the Land Snails of Britain and North-west Europe*. Collins, 1979.

Kerney, M. P., and Stubbs, A. *The Conservation of Snails, Slugs and Freshwater Mussels*. Nature Conservancy Council, 1980.

SOCIETY
The Conchological Society of Great Britain and Ireland. Honorary Secretary: Dr M. B. Seddon, School of Geography and Geology, College of St Paul and St Mary, The Park, Cheltenham, Gloucestershire GL50 2RH.

Identification table

Species are arranged in approximate order of size, largest to smallest but with similar species grouped together in a few cases. Hence by careful measurement (see figure 1), noting the shell shape and then comparing with the other features described, identification should be possible. Size and colour are variable in some species and in general identification is much more reliable if based on a number of individuals rather than on a single specimen. All information relates to adult snails.

Name	Typical height and breadth in mm; Shell shape and approximate number of whorls	Colour of shell	Habitat and distribution	Distinguishing features and similar species
Helix pomatia Roman Snail	40 x 40 Globular 6	Pale yellow, occasionally with faint brown spiral bands.	Widespread in woods, hedges and downland, calcareous districts in southern England.	Very large size, coarse transverse ridges, has a small umbilicus. *Helix aspersa.*
Helix aspersa Common Snail	30 x 30 Globular 5	Usually brown with paler flecks and up to 5 darker spiral bands.	Widely distributed.	Large size, flecking, wrinkled surface to shell. Lacks umbilicus *Helix pomatia, Arianta arbustorum.*
Cepaea nemoralis Brown-lipped Banded Snail	18 x 22 Globular 5½	Very variable (see text). Yellow, pink or brown with up to 5 dark spiral bands.	Widely distributed.	Large size, bright colours. Lip normally brown (see text). *Cepaea hortensis.*
Cepaea hortensis White-lipped Banded Snail	14 x 17 Globular 5½	Variable. Normally yellow with up to 5 dark spiral bands (see text).	Widely distributed.	Large size, bright colours. Lip normally white (see text). *Cepaea nemoralis.*
Arianta arbustorum Copse Snail	16 x 21 Globular 5	Brown or yellowish, paler flecks, single brown peripheral band.	Often in moist woodland. Widely distributed.	Brown peripheral band, large size. But small compared with *Helix aspersa.*
Theba pisana Sandhill Snail	15 x 18 (variable) Globular 5½	Variable, white to ginger, often with dark interrupted spiral bands or striations.	Very uncommon. Coastal dunes in southern Britain.	Spiral striations and restricted distribution. *Cernuella virgata.*
Monacha cantiana Kentish Snail	12 x 16 Globular 6	Off-white to brownish or reddish pink with paler peripheral band.	Scrub and long grass. Widely distributed but commoner in the south and east.	White rib inside shell mouth. H a small umbilicus. Pink forms *Cepaea nemoralis.*
Helicella itala Heath Snail	9 x 18 (variable) Sub-globular to discoidal 6	Variable, commonly white with one or more dark spiral bands.	Dunes, calcareous grassland. Commoner in the south.	Large umbilicus, ⅓ diameter shell. *Cernuella virgata.*
Helicigona lapicida Lapidary Snail	8 x 16 Discoidal 5½	Usually light brown with darker broad transverse marks.	Various habitats in calcareous districts. North to Yorkshire.	Pronounced keel.
Cernuella virgata Striped Snail	8 x 15 (very variable) Globular 6	Variable. Most often white with one dark brown peripheral band.	Dunes and calcareous grassland. Commoner in southern Britain.	Thick globular shell with a s umbilicus. *Helicella itala.*
Trichia striolata Strawberry Snail	9 x 12 Sub-globular 6	Usually reddish brown with a pale peripheral band.	Widespread.	Shell slightly keeled with no in adults. *Trichia hispida.*
Pomatias elegans Round-mouthed Snail	15 x 10 Conical 4½	Grey-brown.	Loose soils in calcareous districts north to Yorkshire.	Very thick strong shell reminiscent of a winkle. T calcareous operculum.
Succinea putris Amber Snail	16 x 10 Conical 3	Greenish-yellow.	Wetland, moist grassland. North to central Scotland.	Thin shell. Animal usually yellow (see text). *Oxyloma pfeifferi.*
Oxyloma pfeifferi Pfeiffer's Amber Snail	10 x 6 Conical 3	Amber to light brown.	Wetland. Widely distributed.	Thin shell. Animal usually grey (see text). *Succinea pu*
Cochlicella acuta Pointed Snail	15 x 6 (variable) Tall conical 9	Variable white to ginger often with a brown spiral band.	Dunes. South and west coasts and Ireland.	Shape and habitat.

22

Name	Typical height and breadth in mm; Shell shape and approximate number of whorls	Colour of shell	Habitat and distribution	Distinguishing features and similar species
Cochlodina laminata Plaited Door Snail	16 x 4 Spindle 11	Fairly glossy brown.	Chiefly woodland. Almost entirely restricted to England.	Sinistral, large size, absence of distinct transverse ridges. Clausilia bidentata, Macrogastra rolphii.
Macrogastra rolphii Rolph's Door Snail	13 x 3.5 Spindle 9	Brown.	Chiefly woodland. Southern England.	Sinistral, distinct transverse ribs, proportionately broad. Cochlodina laminata, Clausilia bidentata.
Clausilia bidentata Door Snail	10 x 2.5 Spindle 11	Brown.	Widespread in woodland and also hedges, rock outcrops and walls.	Sinistral, regular transverse ribs. Smaller than Cochlodina laminata and Macrogastra rolphii.
Balea perversa Tree Snail	8 x 2.5 Tall conical 8	Pale yellow-brown.	Rock outcrops and stone walls. Only occasionally on trees. Widely distributed.	Sinistral, pale colour, club-shaped, squarish mouth with no teeth. Juveniles of Cochlodina laminata, Clausilia bidentata and Macrogastra rolphii are also club-shaped.
na obscura Lesser Bulin	8 x 4 Tall conical 6½	Brown.	Woodland and scrub. Widely distributed.	Size and shape. Reflected white lip with no teeth.
Candidula intersecta Wrinkled Snail	6.5 x 10 Sub-globular 6	Variable. Usually white to ginger. Dark brown interrupted spiral bands.	Dunes and grassland. More common in southern Britain.	Thick shell. Strong transverse growth ridges. Candidula gigaxii.
Candidula gigaxii Eccentric Snail	6 x 10 Sub-globular 5	Variable. Usually white to light brown with darker spiral markings.	Dunes, grassland and sometimes hedgerows. More common in southern Britain.	Thick shell. Fine transverse ridges. Eccentric umbilicus (see text). Candidula intersecta.
nobiella rufescens Brown Snail	6 x 9 Globular 4½	Pale brown.	Old, moist woodland. Northern and western Britain.	Very thin, flexible shell. No peripheral band, no hairs. Trichia hispida and juvenile Arianta arbustorum.
Ashfordia granulata Silky Snail	6 x 8 Globular 5½	Pale brown to grey-yellow, often with dark spots on body of animal visible through shell.	Locally distributed in moist woodland.	Thin shell, straight hairs with bulbous bases. Very small umbilicus. Trichia hispida.
Trichia hispida Hairy Snail	5 x 8 (variable) Sub-globular 6	Brown.	Widely distributed.	Short curved hairs covering shell in fresh specimens. Usually some remain around umbilicus in older shells. Ashfordia granulata, Trichia striolata.
Oxychilus cellarius Cellar Snail	5 x 10 Discoidal 6	Very pale glossy brown. (Animal pale blue-grey.)	Widely distributed.	Oxychilus alliarius, Aegopinella nitidula. (Also an uncommon species, Oxychilus draparnaudi, breadth 11-16, which has a dark cobalt blue body.)
Aegopinella nitidula Smooth Snail	4 x 8 Discoidal 4½	Light brown.	Widely distributed.	Shell waxy rather than glossy. Often whitish around umbilicus. Oxychilus cellarius, Oxychilus alliarius, Zonitoides nitidus.
Zonitoides nitidus Shiny Snail	3.5 x 7 Discoidal 4½	Glossy brown but animal dark, making shell appear black.	Wetlands. Widely distributed.	Orange spot on mantle visible through shell. Oxychilus alliarius, Aegopinella nitidula. (Also Z. excavatus, acid woodland, animal paler, umbilicus ¼ or more shell diameter.)
Oxychilus alliarius Garlic Snail	3 x 6 Discoidal 4½	Very glossy brown.	Common. Widely distributed.	Smells strongly of garlic when touched. Oxychilus cellarius, Aegopinella nitidula, Zonitoides nitidus. (Also O. helveticus, 4 x 9 mm, little or no smell of garlic.)

Name	Typical height and breadth in mm; Shell shape and approximate number of whorls	Colour of shell	Habitat and distribution	Distinguishing features and similar species
Discus rotundatus Rounded Snail	3 x 6 Discoidal 6	Pale yellow-brown, broad reddish transverse bands.	Common. Widely distributed.	Colour pattern, regularly spaced transverse ribs, umbilicus 1/3 shell diameter.
Vitrina pellucida Pellucid Snail	3 x 5 Sub-globular 3	Translucent green.	Common. Widely distributed.	Animal has a lobe of the mantle reflected up on to the outer surface of shell.
Cochlicopa lubrica Slippery Snail	6 x 2.5 Sub-cylindrical 5½	Translucent glossy brown.	Common. Widely distributed.	Very glossy shell, with no teeth in mouth. *Azeca goodalli.*
Azeca goodalli Three-toothed Snail	6 x 2.5 Spindle 7	Very glossy brown.	Chiefly woods. Local in England and Wales.	Flat-sided whorls result in a cigar like outline. Mouth with up to small teeth. *Cochlicopa lubrica.*
Cecilioides acicula Blind Snail	5 x 1.2 Cylindrical 5	Colourless or white.	Subterranean. Chiefly open, calcareous habitats. Southern Britain.	Shell mouth large, about 1/3 o shell height.
Lauria cylindracea Chrysalis Snail	4 x 2 Cylindrical 6	Fairly glossy brown.	Common. Widely distributed.	Shell mouth has a flat, white lip *Leiostyla anglica, Pupilla muscorum.*
Leiostyla anglica English Chrysalis Snail	3.5 x 2 Oval 6	Rich red-brown.	Chiefly damp woodland. Northern and western Britain.	Colour. Mouth with up to 6 teeth *Lauria cylindracea, Pupilla muscorum.*
Pupilla muscorum Moss Snail	3.5 x 1.7 Cylindrical 6	Dull brown.	Dunes, dry calcareous habitats. Less common in northern Britain.	Pale rib on outside of shell, ju behind mouth. *Lauria cylindracea, Leiostyla anglica.*
Euconulus fulvus Tawny Snail	2.5 x 3 Top-shaped 5	Translucent yellow-brown.	Common. Widely distributed.	Silky sheen when fresh. Anim pale grey-brown. *Euconulus alderi.*
Euconulus alderi (no English name)	2 x 2.5 Top-shaped 5	Glossy brown.	Wetland and stream sides. Widely distributed.	Animal dark, making shell appe black when withdrawn. *Euconulus fulvus.*
Vitrea crystallina Crystal Snail	1.7 x 3.5 Discoidal 5	Colourless, tinged green.	Common. Widely distributed.	Supporting rib just inside shel mouth. (*V. contracta,* 1.2 x 2 mm, has no rib.)
Acanthinula aculeata Prickly Snail	2 x 2 Globular 4	Dark brown.	Chiefly woodland. Fairly widespread.	Fresh shells have large, regula spaced spines around peripher These wear down with age. *Spermodea lamellata.*
Spermodea lamellata Plaited Snail	2 x 2 Globular (beehive shaped) 5½	Pale golden brown.	Old woodland. Restricted almost entirely to northern Britain.	Fresh shells iridescent due to close, regularly spaced transve ridges. *Acanthinula aculeata.*
Pyramidula rupestris Rock Snail	1.5 x 2.5 Top-shaped 4	Purplish brown to light grey.	Calcareous rocks and walls. Locally distributed.	Colour, pronounced transvers ridges, very large umbilicus 1/2 shell diameter.
Vallonia costata Ribbed Snail	1.2 x 2.5 Discoidal 3¼	Grey-white.	Dry open calcareous habitats. Less common in northern Britain.	Very large, regularly spaced transverse ribs. Mouth with v large white lip. (Two very sim species *V. excentrica* and *V. pulchella* lack the ribs.)
Acicula fusca Point Shell	2.5 x 0.8 Cylindrical 5	Translucent golden brown.	Damp parts of old woodland. Local.	Small, horny operculum (not obvious). Widely, unevenly spaced transverse grooves in sh
Vertigo species Whorl Snails	2 x 1 Oval to barrel-shaped 5	Brown.	A number of species in this group of very small snails oc in a variety of habitats. Identification of species is no easy. Most bear teeth in the shell mouth. *Columella edentula* and *C. aspera* (about 3 x 1.5 mm) are similar lack teeth.	
Carychium tridentatum and *C. minimum* Herald Snails	2 x 1 Spindle 4 to 5	White or colourless.	*C. minimum* in wet-lands. *C. tridentatum* also in slightly drier places.	Thick lip bearing 3 teeth. (See text.)
Punctum pygmaeum Dwarf Snail	0.8 x 1.5 Discoidal 3½	Golden brown.	Chiefly woodland. Widely distributed.	Very small size. Young *Discu rotundatus* are superficially sin but have proportionately few whorls.